C000259303
Hi, Look at this fab picture of me singing at my favourite place - the Karaoke Café! Why don't you make me look like a pop star by colouring in my clothes with some really funky styles and patterns.....and don't forget the glitter to make me really sparkle!!
When you have finished, don't forget to complete your details on the back of this page and send it to me at the address shown!
Good luck,
Sindy x

Contents

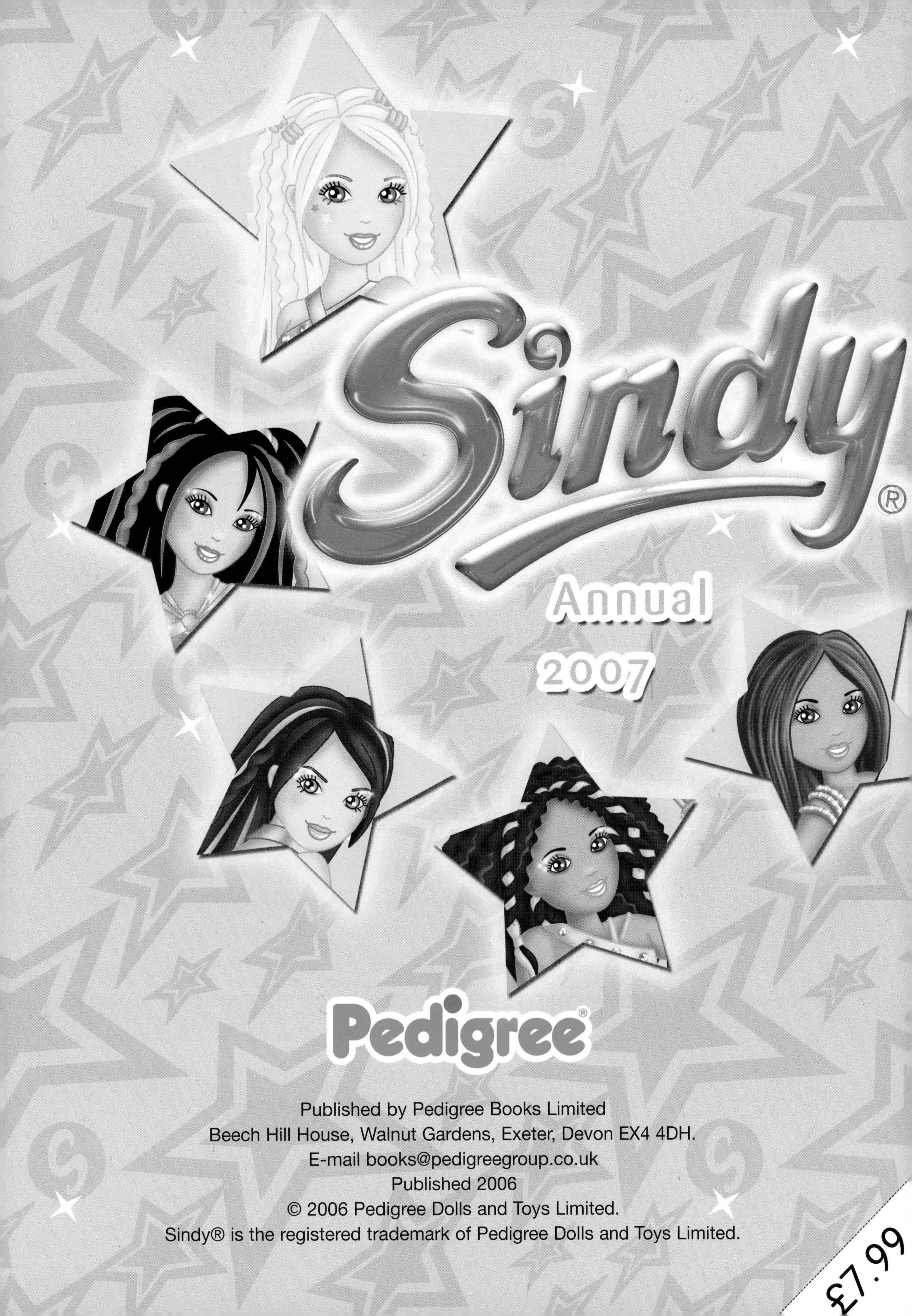

Published by Pedigree Books Limited
Beech Hill House, Walnut Gardens, Exeter, Devon EX4 4DH.
E-mail books@pedigreegroup.co.uk
Published 2006

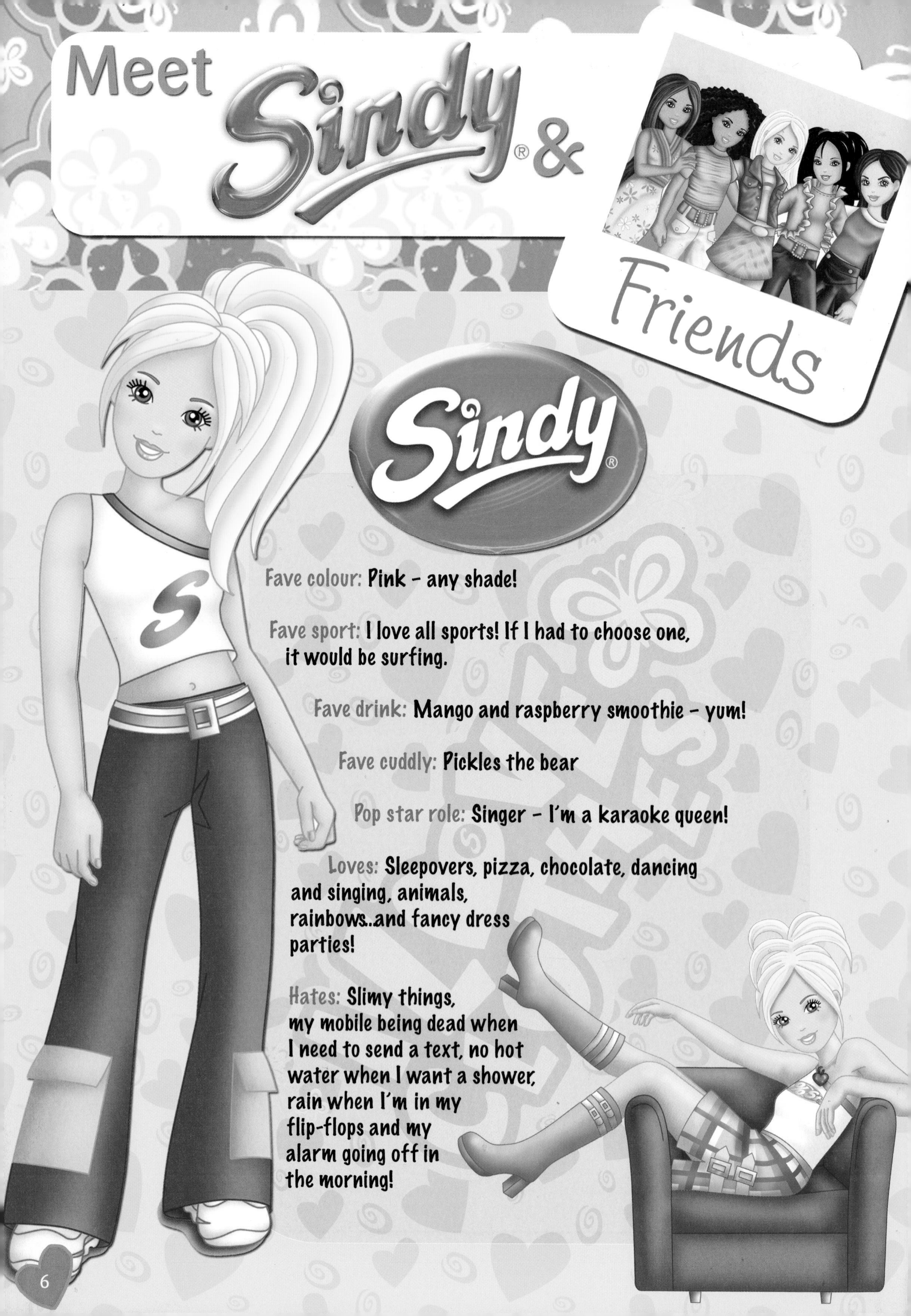

Meet Sindy® & Friends

Sindy®

Fave colour: Pink - any shade!

Fave sport: I love all sports! If I had to choose one, it would be surfing.

Fave drink: Mango and raspberry smoothie - yum!

Fave cuddly: Pickles the bear

Pop star role: Singer - I'm a karaoke queen!

Loves: Sleepovers, pizza, chocolate, dancing and singing, animals, rainbows..and fancy dress parties!

Hates: Slimy things, my mobile being dead when I need to send a text, no hot water when I want a shower, rain when I'm in my flip-flops and my alarm going off in the morning!

Fave colour: Orange

Fave sport: Kick-boxing. I'd love to learn how to break-dance, too!

Fave drink: Apple juice

Fave cuddly: Cookie the puppy

Pop star role: Drummer

Loves: Dancing, taking photos with my digital camera, making scrapbooks, raspberry ripple ice-cream and lie-ins on Saturdays.

Hates: Smelly dogs, maths homework, people who are rude, spiders and having to breathe in traffic fumes when I'm trying to shop!

Fave colour: Blue

Fave sport: Any!

Fave drink: Banana milkshake

Fave cuddly: Flopsey the rabbit

Pop star role: Saxophonist

Loves: Roller-blading, getting up and out early at weekends, a hot shower after playing sports, winning a match, the sea.

Hates: Smoky places, losing a match, biscuits with nuts in, jealous people, seaweed and..laziness!

Rosa

Fave colour: Red

Fave sport: I hate the cold, so winter sports are out! Tennis is okay.

Fave drink: Cranberry and raspberry juice..today!

Fave cuddly: Stomp the elephant

Pop star role: Keyboard player

Loves: Salsa dancing, making up my own recipes, the summer, writing songs on my keyboard, silver jewellery, excitement!

Hates: Big animals, silly ring tones, falling out with friends, being bored, stinging nettles, the cold and mushy food.

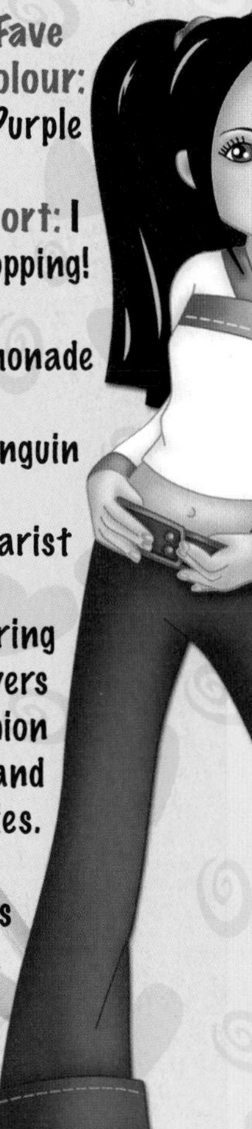

Fave colour: Purple

Fave sport: I don't do sports, only shopping!

Fave drink: Strawberry lemonade

Fave cuddly: Pom Pom the penguin

Pop star role: Guitarist

Loves: Shopping, pampering myself, doing makeovers on friends, reading fashion mags, customising clothes and accessories.

Hates: My hair taking ages to dry, leaving home without my mirror, homework and new shoes giving me blisters.

Maze To The Mall
Sindy is going to meet Mya, Lilli, Emma and Rosa to spend the afternoon at the mall. Which way should she go to join her friends?
Start
The Mall

Catching Up

Mya has called in at Sindy's to catch up on the latest gossip!

Look at the two pictures and see if you can spot the five differences between them. The answers are at the bottom of the page.

Answers: One of Sindy's skirt buckles is missing, Sindy's bag has moved, Mya's sunglasses have disappeared, there is a line missing from Mya's jeans, a compact has appeared.

Stepping Out

Sindy loves to organise trips for her friends and is taking them to a summer music festival!

With Sindy

Use your crayons or pens to colour this picture of Sindy and the girls, copying the colours from the opposite page.

Snug Sunnies

Sunnies are your must-have summer accessory, so make sure you look after them! If the case you got with your pair is a bit dull, or you've lost it altogether, make your own funky customised case to keep those stylish shades scratch-free!

You'll need:
Felt in your fave colour
Safe glue
Glitter
Sequins or small beads
Lace trim

All you need to do is:

1. Ask a grown-up to help you cut a rectangle of felt about 20cm wide by 16cm long.

2. Spread glue along the edge of one short side and at least half way along the edge of one longer side.

3. Fold the felt in half widthways to make your case shape and put a heavy book on top to press it down while the glue dries.

3. Decorate your case with the glitter and sequins or small beads. You could stick sequins in a heart shape or your name's initial letter.

4. Add a lace trim round the top and you have a cool case to keep your sunnies safe and snug in!

Ballerina Sindy

Sindy loves going to ballet classes and especially enjoys rehearsing for a show! Look at all the dancing shadows and say which one matches Sindy exactly. The answer is at the bottom of the page.

1

2

3

4

5

Answer: Number 4

Party In The Park

It was a warm, sunny day in the middle of the summer holidays and Sindy had arranged a trip to a theme park. She and her friends arrived early so they could get into the park as soon as it opened.

"How much further do we have to walk?" moaned Lilli, as they made their way along the seemingly endless path from the car park.

"Well, maybe you should have worn more sensible shoes," Sindy teased. "Fancy wearing heels to go on rides!"

"I wanted to look my best," Lilli grinned. "You never know where you might be spotted!"

"No one's going to come here to star spot," scoffed Emma. "There are thousands of people already and it's only early!"

When they finally reached the entrance, there were long queues for tickets. It seemed that everyone had the same idea.
"Don't worry, girls," smiled Sindy, heading for a kiosk with a short queue. "My dad pre-booked the tickets for us, so we just need to collect them."
"This place is massive!" gasped Rosa, once they were through the turnstiles. "Where do we start?"
Sindy gave maps to everyone and they looked at the list of rides.
"Log flume first!"
"No, roller coaster first!"
"Ghost train! Ghost train!"
"Shush!" cried Sindy. "We need to go on the busiest rides first, while people are still waiting to come in."
The five girls agreed that they would go on the new roller coaster they had seen advertised as the fastest in Europe.

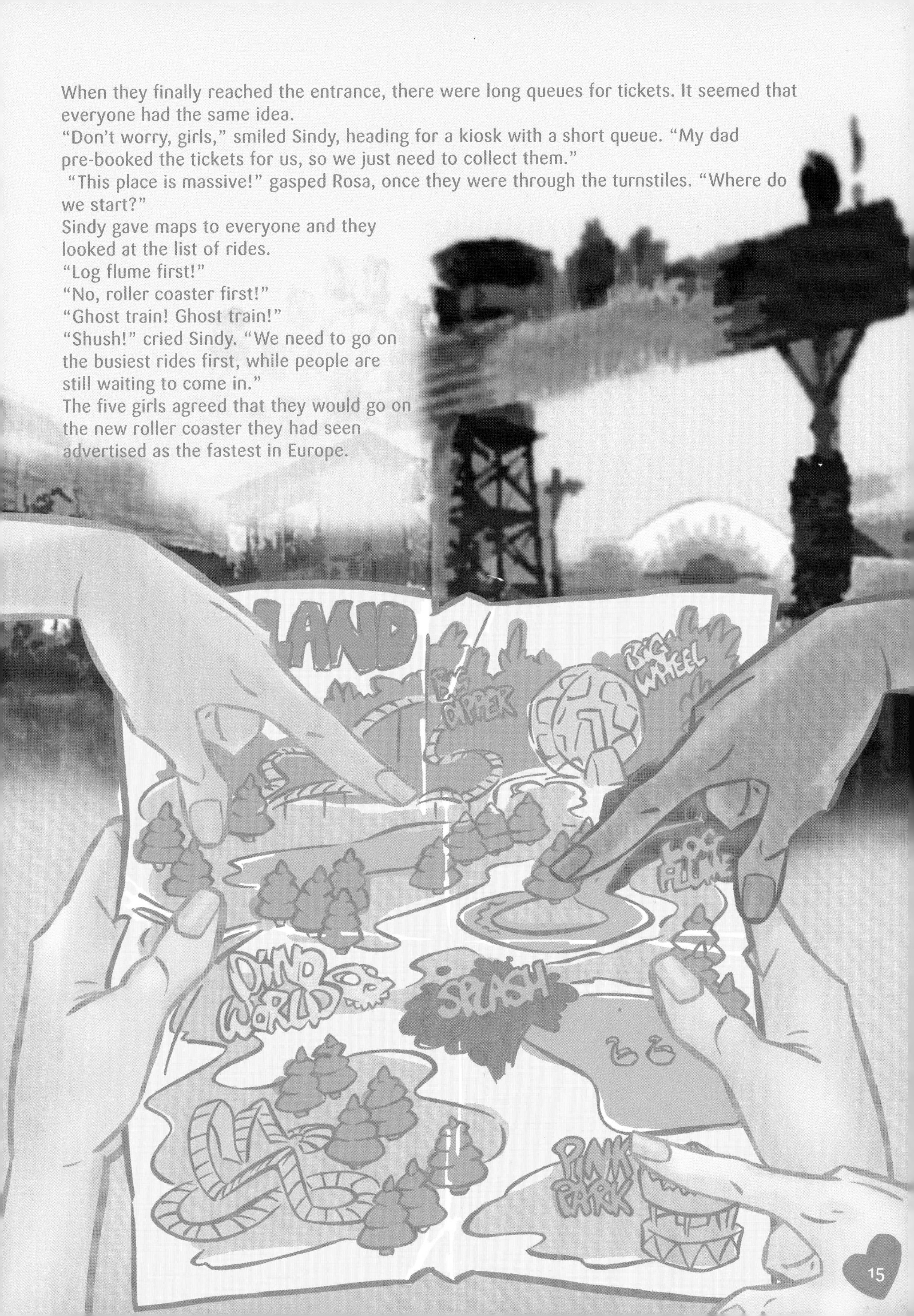

"Madre mia!" exclaimed Rosa when they reached the ride. "There's a fifteen minute wait!"
"That's why we've come here first," Sindy explained. "It'll be a two hour wait by lunchtime!"
The girls joined the queue and before they knew it, they were climbing aboard.
"Um, I think I've changed my mind," Mya said nervously, as the carriage bars locked in position.
"Too late!" shrieked Emma, as they whizzed forward. The girls screamed excitedly with the ride's every twist and turn, raising their arms on the steep drops. It was all over in two minutes.
"Man, that was fast!" giggled Emma, staggering off the ride and holding on to Sindy for support. "My legs have gone all wobbly!"

"Okay, what's next?" asked Mya eagerly, getting into the swing of things.
"Well, Glide's pretty popular," Sindy replied, peering at her map. "It's this way, follow me."
The girls had to queue for a little longer this time, but the time soon went as they chattered and giggled. At last they were on and strapped into place.
"What happens on this one?" asked Emma.
"This!" yelled Sindy, as their seats tipped forward and they sped along.
"We're flying!" cried Lilli, spreading out her arms and cackling as they glided high above the park. They glimpsed people waving as they swooped down over them, but had no time to react as they sped upwards again.
"That was fantastic!" Mya exclaimed as they climbed off.

The girls decided to go on one more ride before grabbing a snack and voted for the log flume.
"Will we get wet?" asked Rosa, as they climbed on.
"What do you think?" giggled Sindy. They set off at a fairly leisurely pace, then began to go upwards.
"This is going really high!" Mya exclaimed. The carriage stopped at the top of a steep slope and the girls screamed as it paused before hurtling down into the water with a huge splash.
"Yeeeuurgh!" shrieked Sindy, getting soaked. They scrambled off and everyone was wet except Rosa.
"So it wasn't such a stupid question," she said, wagging her finger at Sindy.
"I can't believe you stayed dry!" laughed Sindy. "It's a miracle!"

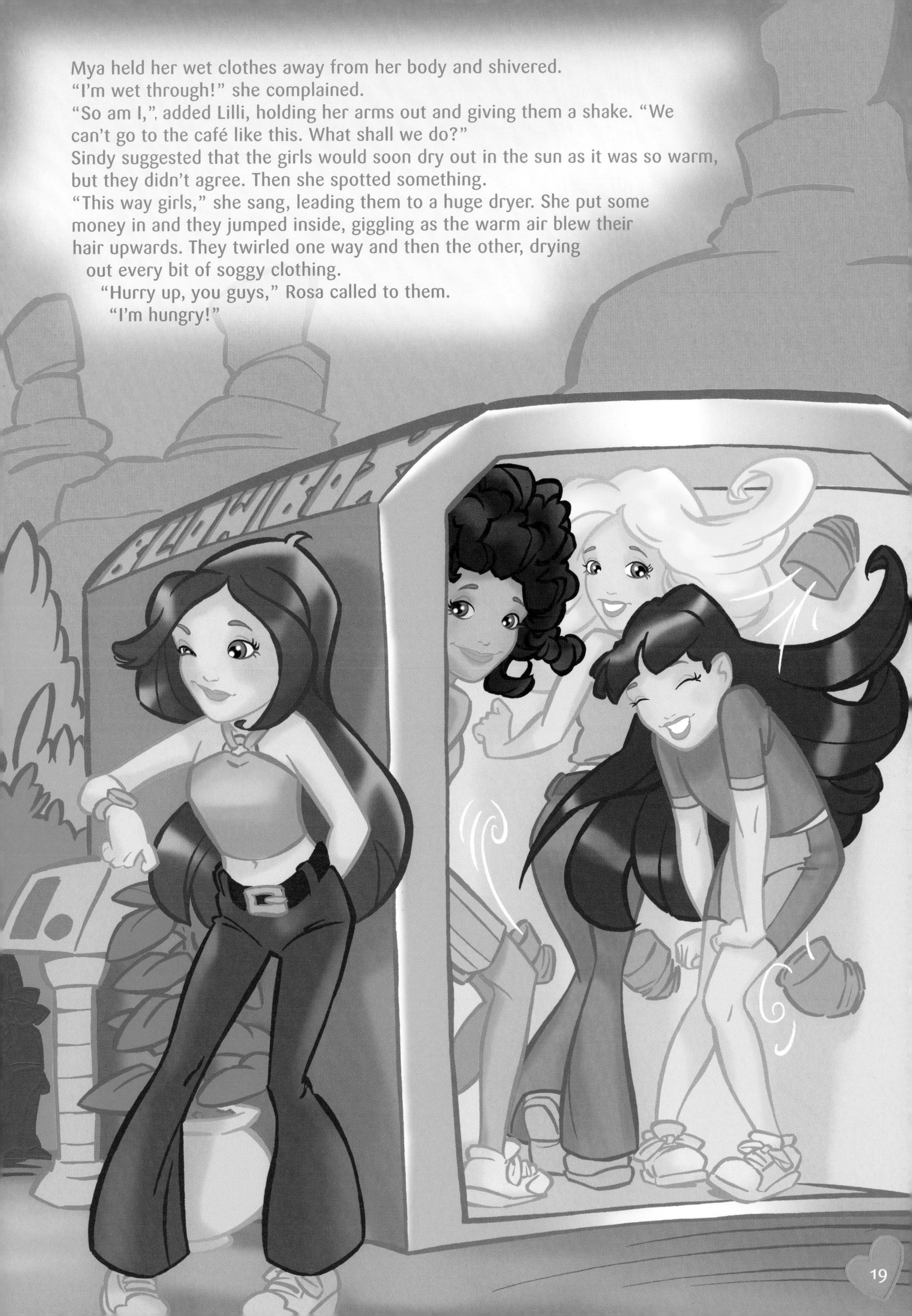

Mya held her wet clothes away from her body and shivered.
“I’m wet through!” she complained.
“So am I,”, added Lilli, holding her arms out and giving them a shake. “We can’t go to the café like this. What shall we do?”
Sindy suggested that the girls would soon dry out in the sun as it was so warm, but they didn’t agree. Then she spotted something.
“This way girls,” she sang, leading them to a huge dryer. She put some money in and they jumped inside, giggling as the warm air blew their hair upwards. They twirled one way and then the other, drying out every bit of soggy clothing.
“Hurry up, you guys,” Rosa called to them. “I’m hungry!”

Rosa led the way to one of the cafes and they all bought muffins and drinks.
"Where were the chocolate ones?" asked Emma as she sat down. "I didn't see the chocolate ones."
"I got the last one," Mya smiled smugly.
"Oh, let me have a bit," said Emma, reaching over to steal a piece. As she leaned past Rosa, she knocked a bottle of water over her.
"Yeow! Emma!" shrieked Rosa, jumping up. "That's cold! Look, I'm soaked now!"
"Told you you'd get wet," giggled Sindy. "Looks like you're not missing out on the dryer experience after all!"
Rosa sighed and went off to get dry.
"And keep your hands off my blueberry muffin, Emma," she called back.

Once Rosa had come back from her all-over blow-dry, Sindy looked at the map and chose the next big ride. They were almost on it when Emma mentioned the upside down bit.
"Upside down bit?" echoed Mya. "You didn't say anything about going upside down!"
"Come on, don't be a wuss," Sindy teased, clambering into a seat. "It's another new experience!"
Mya braced herself as the ride raced forward and hurtled round a twisting track, sending them upside down once, twice, three times!
"Ew, I think we should have gone on that before we had muffins," groaned Lilli when they came off.
"Actually, it wasn't as bad as I thought it would be," Mya said brightly, happy to be back on the ground.

As the girls wandered along, talking and laughing, Sindy noticed a little boy standing on his own. He looked as if he was about to cry.
"Hello," she smiled, stopping and crouching down to talk to him. "Are you all right?"
"No!" the boy shook his head and burst into tears. Sindy gave him a tissue and told him she could help.
"I've lost my mum and dad," he sobbed. "I came off a ride with them and then they disappeared."
"Come with me," said Sindy, holding out her hand. "I know someone who can help find Mum and Dad." She looked up to see her friends were ahead, not realising she had stopped.
"Wait a minute, guys!" she called. "We just need to do a little detour!"

The girls hurried back and fussed over the little boy. As they ushered him to the Lost Children office, he told them his name was Thomas. By the time they reached the office, he knew all their names, too.

“This is Thomas,” Sindy told the woman there. “We found him by Cannonball Mountain.”

“Don’t worry, Thomas,” the woman smiled. “You’ll soon be enjoying your day again. I’m going to talk into this microphone so everyone in the park can hear it, then your mum and dad will come and find you. Okay?”

“Okay,” Thomas nodded, his wide eyes still glistening with tears. The announcement had hardly begun when his mother came running up.

“Thomas!” she cried, scooping him up and hugging him. “I was hoping I’d find you here.”

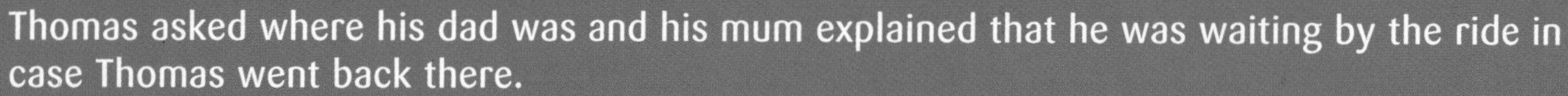

Thomas asked where his dad was and his mum explained that he was waiting by the ride in case Thomas went back there.
"I don't know how we managed to lose you, Tom," she added. "You must have gone out of the ride the wrong way."
"It was all right because my friend Sindy looked after me," said Thomas, pulling at Sindy's hand.
"Thank you so much," Tom's mum said, turning to Sindy. "Have you and your friends had lunch yet?"
"Well...no," said Sindy. To her delight, she and her friends were invited to the best restaurant in the park. They followed Tom and his mum inside and were greeted with cheers from the rest of the family.

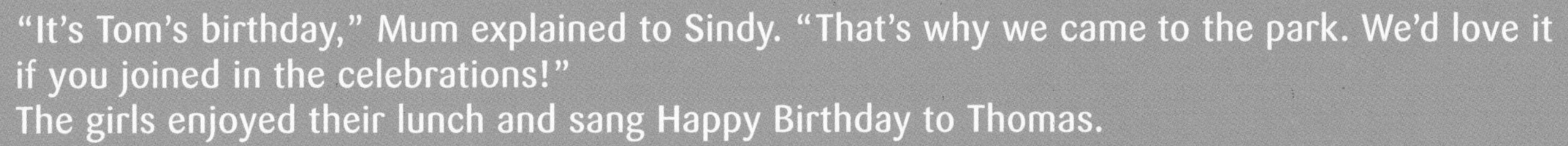

"It's Tom's birthday," Mum explained to Sindy. "That's why we came to the park. We'd love it if you joined in the celebrations!"
The girls enjoyed their lunch and sang Happy Birthday to Thomas.
"Will you help me blow out my candles?" he asked.
"If you let us have a teensy bit of your cake," grinned Sindy. They all counted to three and blew.
"Now make a wish," Sindy whispered. Tom squeezed his eyes shut and opened them again.
"I wish that Sindy could be my pen friend!" he declared, making everyone laugh. He looked at Sindy expectantly. "Will you write to me?" he asked.
Sindy ruffled his hair fondly.
"I love to," she smiled. "And I'll use a souvenir pen from here to do it!"

Park Puzzle

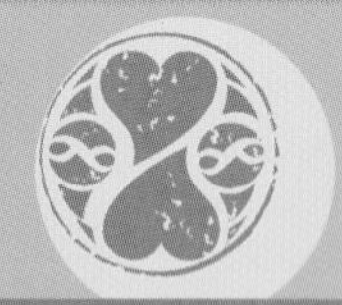

Sindy and her friends had the best time at the theme park! See if you can find their names in the square and then look for all these park words - they read up, down, backwards, forwards and diagonally.

M	E	R	R	Y	G	O	R	O	U	N	D
T	Y	L	O	G	F	L	U	M	E	S	N
C	J	A	S	M	A	E	R	C	E	C	I
A	H	S	N	O	O	L	L	A	B	O	A
N	S	E	I	H	T	O	O	M	S	A	R
D	L	D	Z	V	S	H	L	M	J	S	T
Y	I	A	S	X	I	P	G	E	B	T	T
F	L	C	H	B	N	L	U	Y	K	E	S
L	L	R	O	P	D	W	J	C	R	R	O
O	I	A	P	G	Y	R	O	S	A	Z	H
S	T	R	O	L	L	E	R	H	P	E	G
S	E	L	P	P	A	E	E	F	F	O	T

SINDY
LOG FLUME
EMMA
GHOST TRAIN

LILLI
TEACUPS
ROSA
ARCADES

MYA
BOATS
CANDY FLOSS
BALLOONS

TOFFEE APPLES
SMOOTHIES
ICE CREAMS
PARK

ROLLER
COASTER
MERRY GO ROUND
SHOP

A Note For Sindy

Sindy is delighted to see that she has got a note from Tom, the little boy she helped in the theme park! Just for fun, he has written it in code. Use the code below to see what it says. The answer is at the bottom of the page.

1	2	3	4	5	6	7	8	9	10	11	12	13	14	15	16	17	18	19	20	21	22	23	24	25	26
a	b	c	d	e	f	g	h	i	j	k	l	m	n	o	p	q	r	s	t	u	v	w	x	y	z

8.9 19.9.14.4.25!

20.8.1.14.11.19 6.15.18 8.5.12.16.9.14.7 13.5
6.9.14.4 13.25 13.21.13 1.14.4 4.1.4 9.14
20.8.5 16.1.18.11. 9 8.1.4 1 12.15.22.5.12.25
2.9.18.20.8.4.1.25!

12.15.22.5 6.18.15.13

20.15.13

Answer: The note says, 'Hi Sindy! Thanks for helping me find my mum and dad in the park. I had a lovely birthday! Love from Tom'.

Emma

Emma's love for muffins got her into trouble at the theme park! She likes to make her own at home and they're great for parties or sleepovers – try these blueberry muffins out on your friends!

These are a fruity classic. If you can't get blueberries, raspberries are just as scrummy!

You'll need:

375g plain flour
4 teaspoons baking powder
1/2 teaspoon salt
100g granulated sugar
100g soft brown sugar
2 eggs
240ml milk
120ml sunflower oil or corn oil
175g blueberries

All you have to do is:

1. Ask a grown-up to pre-heat the oven to 200° C or Gas Mark 6 while you lay out 12 muffin cases on a muffin tray.
2. Sieve the flour into a bowl and stir in the baking powder, salt and sugar.
3. Beat the egg and oil together in a separate bowl and whisk in the milk.
4. Use a metal spoon to fold the egg mixture into the flour until no flour is visible. There will be lumps but this is fine - if you try and mix them out, your muffins won't rise as well!
5. Gently fold in the blueberries.
6. Spoon the mixture into the muffin cases and bake in the oven for about 25 minutes until risen and golden.
7. Ask a grown-up to take the muffins out of the oven. When they have cooled enough to handle, put them on a wire rack to cool completely.

Get some friends round and hand out your muffins...Mmmmm!

Brilliant blueberries!

- **Blueberries come from North America.**
- **Blueberries are bursting with Vitamin C.**
- **There are about 30 different types of blueberry.**
- **Wild bears love blueberries!**

Stylin' Sindy

Sindy and Lilli are stepping out in style to meet the others in the smoothie bar.

Use your colours to give them fab new looks!

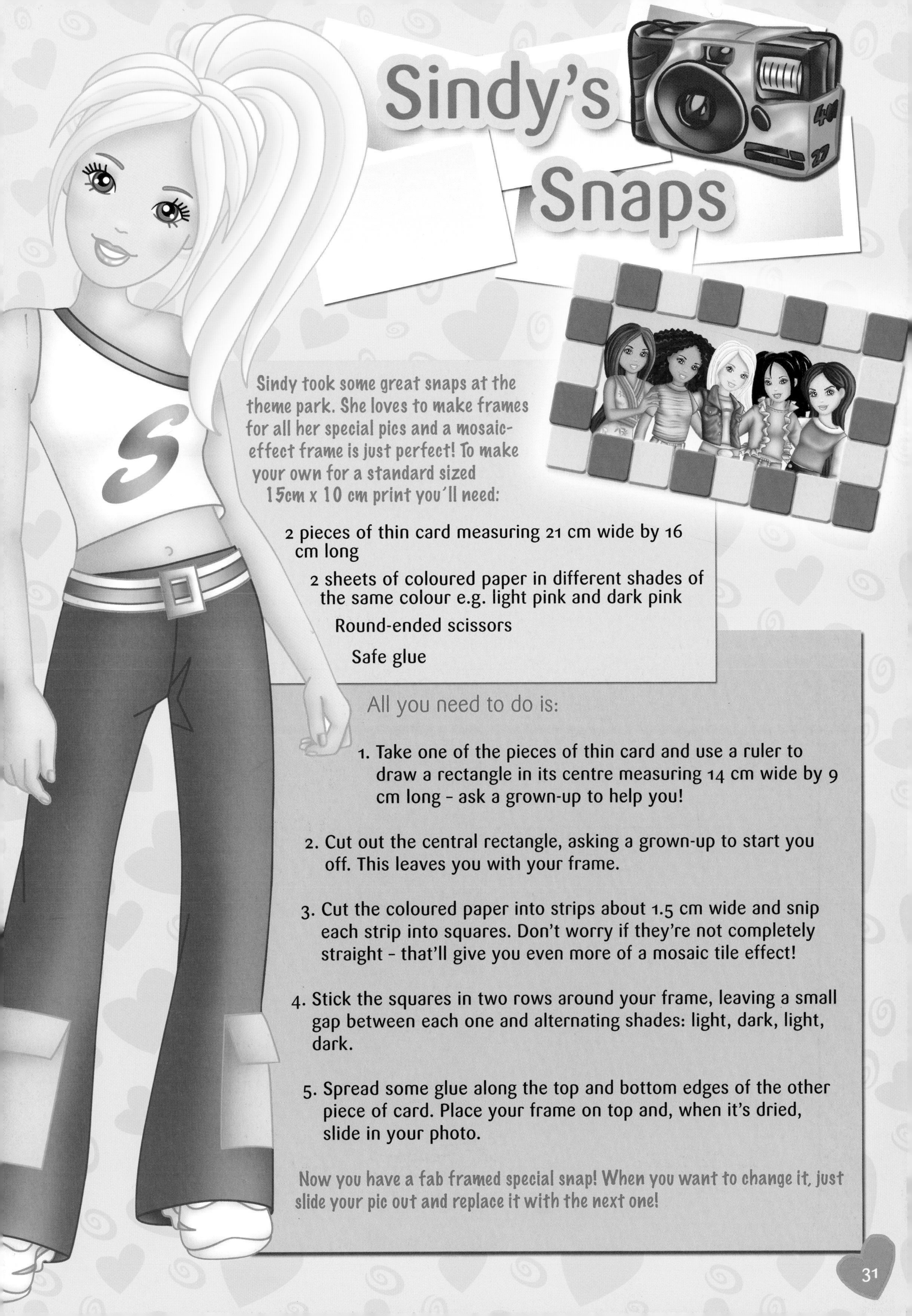

Sindy's Snaps

Sindy took some great snaps at the theme park. She loves to make frames for all her special pics and a mosaic-effect frame is just perfect! To make your own for a standard sized 15cm x 10 cm print you'll need:

- 2 pieces of thin card measuring 21 cm wide by 16 cm long
- 2 sheets of coloured paper in different shades of the same colour e.g. light pink and dark pink
- Round-ended scissors
- Safe glue

All you need to do is:

1. Take one of the pieces of thin card and use a ruler to draw a rectangle in its centre measuring 14 cm wide by 9 cm long - ask a grown-up to help you!
2. Cut out the central rectangle, asking a grown-up to start you off. This leaves you with your frame.
3. Cut the coloured paper into strips about 1.5 cm wide and snip each strip into squares. Don't worry if they're not completely straight - that'll give you even more of a mosaic tile effect!
4. Stick the squares in two rows around your frame, leaving a small gap between each one and alternating shades: light, dark, light, dark.
5. Spread some glue along the top and bottom edges of the other piece of card. Place your frame on top and, when it's dried, slide in your photo.

Now you have a fab framed special snap! When you want to change it, just slide your pic out and replace it with the next one!

Looking For Lippies

Sindy and her friends always make the effort to look good and that means wearing some luscious lippy in one of the latest hot colours!
Look carefully at the picture and see if you can spot a lipstick for each girl.

POP SCHOOL

CONGRATULATIONS!
U R THE 1ST PRIZE WINNER IN THE OP SCHOOL COMP FOR FURTHER INFO, CALL HOLLY ON

WAAAAAAAAAAAH! YES! I'VE WON!

WHAT THE -

ALL RIGHT, CALM DOWN! NOW YOU'VE BURST OUR EARDRUMS, WHY DON'T YOU TELL US WHAT YOU'VE WON?
DON'T YOU REMEMBER? I ENTERED THAT COMPETITION TO BE AT THE FINAL OF POP SCHOOL. I'VE WON...AND I CAN TAKE FOUR FRIENDS!
WAAAAAH! HOORAY! WE'RE GOING TO BE ON THE TELLY...PROBABLY!
YOU KNOW WHAT THIS MEANS, GIRLS...AN EMERGENCY SHOPPING TRIP FOR SOME FUNKY NEW GEAR!
RIGHT!

TWO WEEKS LATER..........
WOW, WE EVEN GET TO GO IN A LIMO? YOU KEPT THAT QUIET,
I'M FULL OF SURPRISES!
AAH, THIS IS THE LIFE. BEING DRIVEN TO TV STUDIOS...
...WITH ALL THE SMOOTHIES YOU CAN DRINK.
IS THERE ANYTHING TO EAT IN HERE?
AT LAST, THEY REACH LONDON...
LOOK, THERE'S THE EYE!
WE'VE BEEN ON THAT!
...AND THE STUDIOS.
STUDIO
AND WE GET TO JUMP THE QUEUE!
LOOK AT ALL THESE PEOPLE!

HI, GIRLS.
I'M HOLLY AND I'LL BE SHOWING YOU AROUND TODAY. WELCOME TO RIVERBANK STUDIOS!
THANKS!
AS THEY APPROACH THE DRESSING ROOMS.....
PSSST, ROSA!
LOOK WHO'S THERE! IT'S STEVEN PIGGELL, ONE OF THE JUDGES!
STEVEN!
HOLA, STEVEN!
ROSA!
HI.

THIS IS STUDIO FOUR, WHERE ALL THE ACTION IS.
I CAN'T BELIEVE YOU JUST DID THAT!
HE SPOKE TO ME, DIDN'T HE? NOW WE ARE AMIGOS!
YOU'LL BE SITTING WITH THE CONTESTANTS' FAMILIES AND FRIENDS AT THE FRONT. THE OTHER SEATS GO TO THE AUDIENCE.
IF THEY'RE LUCKY ENOUGH TO GET IN, RIGHT?
I'M SURE YOU RECOGNISE THE STAGE... GO ON IT IF YOU LIKE. IMAGINE YOU'RE TV STARS!
WOW! GREAT!
THIS IS FAB!
VOTE FOR ME, I'M BRILLIANT!
I'D LOVE TO DANCE ON HERE...

ROSA CAN'T RESIST
A TINKLE ON THE IVORIES...
OH, YOU PLAY WELL!
I KNOW. AND MY FRIEND SINDY SINGS WELL. SHE'S THE KARAOKE QUEEN!
REALLY? DO YOU SING?
WELL, YES... AND THE OTHERS PLAY INSTRUMENTS, TOO.
ON THE SHOW! WOW!
LET ME SET YOU UP WITH SOME STUFF IN A REHEARSAL ROOM. IT WOULD BE GREAT TO HAVE YOU DO A SONG ON THE SHOW!
THE GIRLS ARE SOON HAVING FUN PLAYING AND SINGING...
HEY, THIS IS REALLY GOOD!

STEVEN HEARS THE MUSIC AND COMES TO INVESTIGATE...
HAVE YOU SEEN WHO'S JUST COME IN?
JUST KEEP PLAYING!
WHEN THE GIRLS HAVE FINISHED.......
CLAP
CLAP
WELL DONE, GIRLS! THAT WAS GREAT!
HMM.

STEVEN LEAVES AS SUDDENLY AS HE CAME IN...
IS THAT ALL HE CAN SAY? 'HMM'?
BELIEVE ME, SINDY, 'HMM' IS GOOD COMING FROM STEVEN.
SHE'S RIGHT, SIND. HE'S USUALLY DEAD NASTY TO EVERYONE!
OUR FIRST FINALISTS ARE... THE BANNED BOYS!
WHISTLE
CLAP!
CHEER!
CLAP!
WHISTLE
CHEER!
CLAP!
THE GIRLS TAKE THEIR SEATS FOR THE FINAL..........
THEY WERE BRILLIANT! I'M VOTING FOR THEM...
BUT YOU HAVEN'T SEEN THE OTHERS YET!
WHEN THEY HAVE FINISHED......
THE NEXT ACT IS ON.......
THEY'RE NOT AS GOOD AS US!

I TOLD YOU!
NOW YOU HAVE TO VOTE FOR HIM TWICE TO CANCEL OUT YOUR FIRST VOTE!
ACTUALLY, HE'S BETTER. I'M VOTING FOR HIM.
.......AND THEN ANOTHER.......

AT LAST THE TIME COMES TO ANNOUNCE THE WINNER...........
ALL THE VOTES HAVE BEEN COUNTED. THE WINNING ACT ON POP SCHOOL 2007 IS.....

....

WHY'S SHE TAKING SO LONG? HAS SHE FORGOTTEN?
SSSSSSHHHHHH!

........THE BANNED BOYS!
YES! HOORAY! WE DID IT! YES!
AND WHILE THE BOYS ARE GETTING READY FOR THEIR FINALE, WE HAVE A SONG FROM OUR VIEWERS' COMPETITION WINNERS. PLEASE WELCOME... SINDY AND FRIENDS!
ON THE JUDGES' PANEL.........
THAT'S ABSURD THEY SHOULD'VE BEEN BANNED BEFORE THE COMPETITION STARTED.
SHUT UP, STEVEN. YOU'RE ONLY JEALOUS.
WHISTLE
CLAP!
CHEER!
CLAP!
WHISTLE
CLAP!
CHEER!
THE GIRLS TAKE TO THE STAGE...

...AND PLAY PERFECTLY.
SINDY! SINDY!
IT'S BEEN AMAZING. THANK YOU SO MUCH.
YOU DID FANTASTICALLY WELL, GIRLS. HAVE YOU HAD A GOOD DAY?
WE DON'T WANT TO GO HOME!
BACKSTAGE AFTERWARDS.......
STEVEN! OH, STEVEN! ADIOS, STEVEN!
OH, PLEASE. NOT AGAIN.
AS THE GIRLS ARE LEAVING...

MR NASTY COMES TO SPEAK TO THEM!
WELL DONE, YOU WERE RATHER GOOD. PERHAPS YOU SHOULD AUDITION NEXT YEAR. UM...ADIOS!!
'RATHER GOOD' IS POP SCHOOL SPEAK FOR FABULOUS!
HE SAID WE WERE RATHER GOOD!
DID YOU HEAR THAT? HE LIKED US!
WAS HE ACTUALLY SMILING?
SIGH! HE SAID ADIOS... TO ME!
WE ARE...
...AT LEAST UNTIL TOMORROW!
WHOAH... EVEN THE PRESS ARE TAKING PHOTOS. IT'S LIKE WE'RE REAL STARS!
THE CROWDS ARE THERE TO WAVE OFF SINDY AND FRIENDS...

Superstar Sindy

Sindy wowed the audience of Pop School! Use your colours to design your own superstar look for Sindy. You could add a pattern or writing to her t-shirt and sprinkle on some glitter for extra sparkle. Don't forget to complete the look with make-up and jewellery!

Music Match
Sindy and her friends had a great day at the Pop School studios! Use a pencil to match each girl to the musical item she needed for her television appearance. Look back at the story if you can't remember! The answers are at the bottom of the page.
STAR
Answers: Sindy used the microphone to sing into, Mya played the drum, Emma played the saxophone, Lilli played the guitar and Rosa was on the keyboard.

Making Notes

Once you can play an instrument, it's easy to learn a new one! Unjumble the letters below to find some more instruments that Sindy and her friends would like to learn how to play. The answers are at the bottom of the page.

Answers: 1. Trumpet 2. Flute 3. Oboe 4. Trombone

Make A

Mya loves to get a beat going wherever she is. Make this little hand drum and you can do the same!

You'll need:

- A round cheese triangle box
- Paints
- A pencil
- String
- Large beads
- Sticky tape
- A grown-up!

Funky Hand Drum

All you need to do is:

1. Decorate your cheese box by painting on a funky pattern.
2. When the paint is dry, make sure the lid stays on your box by putting a few short pieces of sticky tape round it.
3. Ask a grown-up to make a hole in the rim of the box so you can stick the pencil through it to make a lollipop shape! (The pencil should sit tightly in the hole so that the box moves with it.)
4. Cut a length of string about 12 cm long and ask a grown-up to make a hole in the centre of the box for it to thread through.
5. Thread your string through, making sure there are equal lengths at each side, and put a bead or two on each end, tying knots to keep them in place.

To play your drum, hold the pencil upright between your palms and roll it to and fro.

The box goes back and forth too and the beads bang against it to make a groovy rhythm! See if you can dance and sing at the same time as you make a beat!

Sindy's Summer Splash

Sindy loved to organise days out in the summer holidays. She and her friends had enjoyed the theme park so much that she looked on the internet to see where else they could spend a fun day. After some searching, she found the ideal place: a water park. It offered every water sport you could think of and even had a man-made beach. On the day the girls went, the weather was perfect.

"Wow! This is just like a real beach!" exclaimed Lilli, taking off her shoes and wriggling her toes in the sand.

"I feel like I'm on holiday," said Rosa, lifting her face to the sun.

"You are on holiday!" Sindy pointed out.

"You know what I mean," giggled Rosa.

The girls laid their towels out on the sand and Sindy asked what they wanted to do first.
“First?” asked Lilli, getting comfortable on her towel and putting on some sun cream. “Well, unless this place has a shopping centre, all I’m doing is sunbathing for the day.”
“Me, too,” agreed Rosa, lying back. “You exercise freaks can do what you want.”
“Does she mean us?” Emma asked Sindy and Mya with mock indignation.
“Let’s leave them to it,” smiled Sindy, “and have some real fun.” She led the others to the information kiosk and they looked through the list of water sports.
“I’ve done water-skiing before,” said Mya. “I don’t know whether to go for that or try something new.”

The three friends decided they would all try something new together and chose kite surfing. Before they could go in the water, they had to have a lesson on land. They were each given boards and kites and practised standing correctly.

"I don't know if I can do this," Sindy giggled, as she wobbled around on the board. "I can't even keep my balance on land!"

"You'll be fine once you get going," said Emma.

"After you've fallen in a few times," Mya added.

Once the lesson had finished, the girls waded into the water to see if they could put into practice what they had learnt. Sindy fell in immediately.

"I told you!" she spluttered, reaching out for her board and trying to climb back on.

Mya and Emma soon got the hang of their new water sport. Their kites caught the wind and pulled them along the water's surface.
"Wheeeee!" Emma shrieked as she glided away. "This is fab!" Not wanting to be outdone, Sindy made a determined effort. She concentrated hard on getting everything right until at last, she too was surfing along with the breeze.
"I'm doing it! Look, I'm doing it!" she shouted eagerly to her friends. As they sailed along, Rosa watched them from the beach.
"Hmm, that looks cool actually," she murmured. She wandered to the water's edge and paddled a little, but decided it was too cold and went back to her comfy towel.
"How's the water?" asked Lilli.
"Cold and wet," Rosa grimaced.

Rosa rummaged in her bag for a magazine and lay on her tummy to read it. A little girl came stumbling through the sand nearby with a bucketful of water and tripped over Rosa's feet, emptying the water all over her back.
"Yeeeow!" shrieked Rosa, jumping up. Startled, the little girl burst into tears and ran to her parents.
"Sorry, little girl!" Rosa called after her. "It's just it was very cold." She saw the girls' parents looking over. "Sorry! I didn't mean to frighten her!" she explained.
"You did scream very loudly," Lilli pointed out. "You even made me jump."
"Well, it was freezing," grumbled Rosa. "She should be apologising to me. I hate cold water and I always end up being covered with it!"

Lilli suggested that they go and have a soak in the warm spa pool. They switched on the jacuzzi bubbles and stepped in.
"Mm, this is nice," sighed Lilli, leaning back into the frothy water.
"Hi, guys," said Sindy, coming to find them. "Mind you don't pull a muscle with all that activity!" She told them how fantastic the kite surfing had been and asked them to come and join in the fun at the water slides.
"I don't want to get wet," said Rosa.
"But you're wet now," Sindy pointed out.
"Ah, but this water is warm, like a bath," explained Rosa. "That's different."
Sindy smiled and shook her head resignedly, leaving the pair to relax a little longer.

Sindy, Mya and Emma meandered round one of the slides on inflatable rings. They looked up to see the highest slide in the park.
"Do we dare go on that?" asked Emma, hearing people scream as they hurtled down the almost vertical drop.
"Of course we dare," scoffed Sindy. "It'll be more exciting than bumbling along in these. They're so tame!" She pushed on the side to spin round on her ring, bumping into Mya, who in turn knocked into Emma, sending her along a little more quickly.
"Ooh, I almost went fast then," giggled Emma. "Do that again!"
The girls laughed as they bumped and spun their way down to the end of the ride.
They scrambled off the rings and gave them back.

"Now it's time for The Big One," grinned Sindy. "Come on!"

"Bring it on!" said Emma, feeling brave. They grabbed a mat each and went up the numerous steps to the top of the slide.

"Oo-er," said Mya. "It looks even steeper from up here."

"That's why we need to go right now!" Sindy exclaimed, grabbing each of her friend's hand. "Here we go girls!" They all shrieked as they flew down the slide together and landed in the splash pool at the end.

"That was excellent!" gasped Mya.

"It's a shame Lilli and Rosa didn't come on," said Emma.

"Those two have been lying around for long enough," said Sindy. "It's time they joined in the fun and games!"

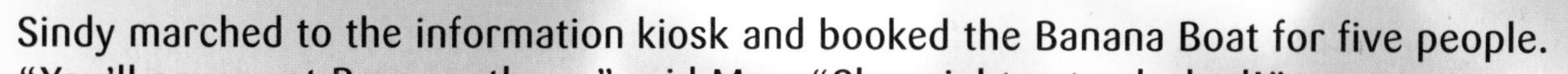

Sindy marched to the information kiosk and booked the Banana Boat for five people.
"You'll never get Rosa on there," said Mya. "She might get splashed!"
"I've booked it now, so she'll have to," Sindy smiled, "and so will Lilli. Come and help me persuade them that it's a good idea."
The three friends went to the beach, where Lilli and Rosa were sunning themselves again.
"Wakey, wakey!" called Sindy, grabbing Rosa by the arm. "Time to have some fun!"
"I am having fun," gasped Rosa, stumbling to her feet. "This is fun for me, seriously!"
"Look," said Sindy, pointing to the Banana Boat bouncing by. "I've booked us all on that, so you have to go on. Let's go!"

Mya and Emma dragged Lilli up from her towel and the two sunbathers begrudgingly agreed to go along with Sindy's plan. They all put lifejackets on while they waited for the Banana Boat to come in and then climbed aboard.
"Hold tight, girls!" called the speedboat driver, starting up the engine. The boat sped off across the water, pulling the yellow boat behind it. The faster they went, the more the banana bobbed up and down as it raced along.
"Tha-a-at's to-o-oo fa-a-ast!" yelled Lilli, hardly able to speak with all the bouncing around. The others only laughed at her wobbly voice. The speedboat curved round in a wide arc and went back to shore. The girls giggled breathlessly as they climbed off.

"That was even better than the big slide," grinned Emma, as they waded to the water's edge. "What did you two lazybones think of it?"

"I'm not lazy!" Lilli protested. "Just...less active than you."

"It was great," said Rosa, "mainly because I didn't get too wet."

Sindy looked at Mya and Emma and raised her eyebrows in an 'are you thinking what I'm thinking?' sort of way. They both nodded and all three jumped on Rosa together, knocking her into the water.

"Yow! You meanies!" she shrieked, trying to keep her hair out of the water. Sindy scooped up some water in her hands and splashed it over Rosa's hair.

"Come on, Rosa!" she laughed. "You have to get wet if you come to a water park!"

They turned to Lilli.
"No, no," said Lilli, walking backwards and putting up her hands. "Don't push me in! I'll push myself in!"
They laughed as Lilli delicately sat down and rolled around in the water, holding her chin up to keep her hair dry.
"You look like a floundering fish!" Sindy exclaimed. They went back to their towels and wrapped themselves up in them. It was almost time to go home.
"I've had the best day, Sindy," said Mya, putting her arm around her friend's shoulder.
"Me, too," added Emma. "Thanks for sorting it out, Sindy." Even Rosa and Lilli agreed that it had been fun.
"Three cheers for Sindy!" said Lilli, and they all shouted together:
"Hip, hip, hooray! Hip, hip, hooray! Hip, hip, hooray!"

Sindy's Super Sports Bars

Sindy loves all kinds of sport and when she's being active, she sometimes needs an energy boost. She likes to make her own sports bars – that way she knows exactly what's in them! Try these recipes to make your own delish snacks to take with you when you're out and about.

Chewy Chocolicious Bars

These bars are easy peasy to make and don't need baking in the oven.

You'll need:

150g oats
100g unsalted butter
125g golden syrup
50g rice pops cereal
100g raisins and/or sultanas
85g milk chocolate, grated

All you need to do is:

1. Mix the oats, rice pops and dried fruit together in a bowl.
2. Ask a grown-up to help you melt the butter and golden syrup together in a saucepan over a low heat.
3. Take the pan off the heat and add the chocolate, stirring gently until it has melted.
4. Pour the mixture on to the oats, rice pops and raisins. Stir in evenly.
5. Press the mixture into a shallow baking tin lined with baking paper, smoothing the top with the back of a metal spoon. Put into the fridge to set.
6. Ask a grown-up to slice up your bars. Keep them in the fridge until you need them.

Yummy!

Fruity Flapjack Bars

These bars need baking, so ask a grown-up to pre-heat the oven to 180° C or Gas Mark 4 before you start.

You'll need:

225g oats
175g brown sugar
175g unsalted butter
2 tablespoons golden syrup
100g dried apricots, chopped

All you need to do is:

1. Ask a grown-up to help you melt the butter, sugar and golden syrup together in a large saucepan over a low heat.
2. Take the pan off the heat and mix in the oats and apricots until they are evenly covered with the butter mixture.
3. Spoon the mixture into a shallow baking tin lined with baking paper and smooth the top with the back of a metal spoon.
4. Ask a grown-up up to put the tin in the middle of the oven and bake for about 20 minutes until golden brown.
5. Ask a grown-up to slice the flapjack mixture into bars while it is still warm (about ten minutes after it has come out of the oven) and leave in the tin to cool.
6. Keep your fruity flapjack bars in a tin until you need them. Delish!

Don't forget to drink plenty of water while you're exercising, especially when outside in the summer!

Fitness Fun

Mya and Emma love all kinds of sport, too.
Use your crayons or pencils to make their sportswear cool and funky!

Sports Search

Sindy and her friends know that sports are not only a good way to keep fit, they're also great fun! Look at this wordsearch square and see if you can find some of the sports that the girls like to take part in. The words read up, down, backwards, forwards and diagonally.

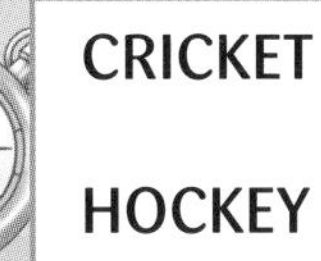

CYCLING
ICE SKATING
BOXING

CRICKET
HOCKEY
ATHLETICS

DANCE
STEP
AEROBICS

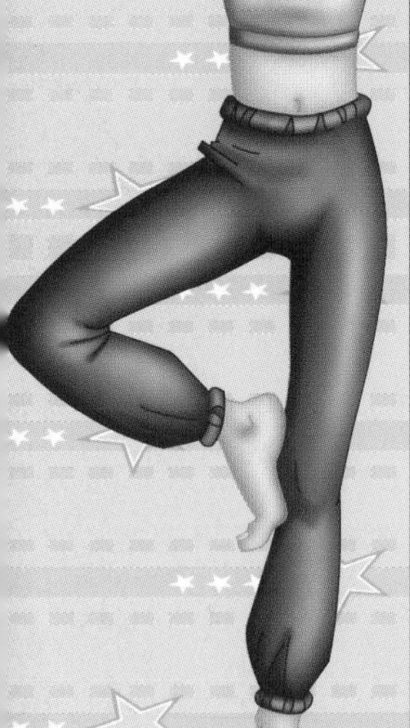

B	A	D	M	I	N	T	O	N	J	M	A
S	O	G	N	I	L	C	Y	C	H	G	T
G	H	X	S	R	E	D	N	U	O	R	H
N	C	R	I	C	K	E	T	Y	C	U	L
I	S	I	N	N	E	T	Z	B	K	N	E
T	M	W	E	I	G	H	T	S	E	N	T
A	E	R	O	B	I	C	S	C	Y	I	I
K	V	B	N	O	H	G	E	A	Q	N	C
S	W	M	D	S	T	E	P	C	U	G	S
E	J	U	L	L	A	B	T	E	N	Q	L
C	J	F	O	O	T	B	A	L	L	A	S
I	G	N	I	M	M	I	W	S	K	T	D

RUNNING
SQUASH
FOOTBALL
WEIGHTS
JUDO

TENNIS
BADMINTON
SWIMMING
ROUNDERS
YOGA
NETBALL

Sindy's Skipathon

Sindy and her friends are doing a skipathon to raise money for their fave charity!

Look at the small pictures at the bottom of these pages and see if you can spot them in the picture of the girls. Tick the box as you find each one.

Water Ways

Rosa is trying a game of tennis and is surprised to find that she's enjoying it! She's taken a break to have a drink of water. Which path should she follow to get to her bottle? The answer is at the bottom of the page.

Answer: Path C

Chocolate Heaven
SINDY IS ORGANISING A SLEEPOVER WITH A CHOCOLATE THEME.................
HERE YOU GO, GUYS. GET READY TO ENTER CHOCOLATE HEAVEN! IN A SEC.
THANKS!
AN EVENING OF CHOCOLATE PAMPERING. FANTASTIC!.
WEAR CHOCOLATE BROWN. AN EXCUSE TO GO SHOPPING, HOORAY!.
COOL INVITATIONS!
VIVA EL CHOCOLATE!!
SEE YOU ALL SATURDAY NIGHT, THEN!
SEE YOU, SINDY!
BYE!

WHEN SATURDAY NIGHT COMES....
TIME FOR US TO GO TO THE RESTAURANT NOW, SINDY. OOH, YOU LOOK NICE!
DO YOU LIKE IT? WE'RE HAVING A CHOCOLATE NIGHT.
OKAY, MUM. 'BYE!
WELL, HAVE A NICE TIME...BUT DON'T MAKE ANY MESS!
LILLI AND MYA ARRIVE SHORTLY AFTERWARDS...
HI, SINDY. I'VE BROUGHT MY SPECIAL CHOCOLATE MUD FACE PACK!
AND THERE'S TONS OF MAKE-UP IN HERE... WARM BROWNS, OF COURSE!
...THEN EMMA AND ROSA MAKE THE PARTY COMPLETE.
LOOK AT ALL THE STUFF ROSA'S BROUGHT!
IT'S TO MAKE CHOCOLATE CAKE AND COOKIES - MY SPECIAL RECIPES, OF COURSE!
WE CAN HAVE HOT CHOCOLATE AND MARSHMALLOWS, TOO!

FACIALS FIRST......
SORRY, BUT IT TICKLES!
EMMA! KEEP STILL, WILL YOU?

EMMA IS CHOCOLATE-COATED, NOW IT'S SINDY'S TURN............
SORRY, LILLI. I JUST SPOTTED AN EARRING ON THE FLOOR. I'LL GET A CLOTH.
THAT'S WHAT YOU CALL A CHOCOLATE DROP!

BUT..............
OH, SINDY! YOU MOVED!
OOH, WHAT'S THAT?
!

IN THE KITCHEN...........
HI, ROSA.
I NEED A CLOTH.
MM, WHAT ARE
YOU MAKING?
CHOCOLATE BLUEBERRY
COOKIES. DELICIOSO!
ARE YOU SURE
CHOCOLATE AND BLUEBERRY
GO TOGETHER?
OF COURSE!
THEN I'LL MAKE THE
CHOCOLATE CARROT
CAKE!
SORRY, SINDY,
I WAS DANCING AND
FORGOT THAT GUNK
WAS THERE!
OO-ER. I THINK
I NEED MORE THAN
A CLOTH NOW.
SINDY GETS A MOP AND
BUCKET.............
I'LL CLEAR IT UP.
COOKIES ARE IN,
NOW FOR THE CAKE!
SORRY ABOUT THE
MESS,
DON'T WORRY.
MUM AND DAD WON'T
BE BACK FOR
AGES YET.

OH, WHAT NOW?
SINDY, I'M SO SORRY. MY NAIL POLISH JUST TIPPED OVER!
THIS TISSUE SEEMS TO BE MAKING IT WORSE...
WELL, OF COURSE IT IS! STOP! YOU CAN'T GET RID OF NAIL POLISH WITH TISSUE. YOU NEED... SOMETHING ELSE!
WHAT ON EARTH DO I NEED TO GET RID OF NAIL POLISH?
SINDY! HELP!
EMMA HAS WASHED OFF HER FACE PACK AND GIVEN THE KITCHEN WALL A CHOCOLATE COATING INSTEAD!
WHAT IS IT - AAARGH! WHAT DID YOU DO?
I THOUGHT I'D MAKE SPECIAL HOT CHOCOLATE IN THE BLENDER FOR EVERYONE BUT...KIND OF... FORGOT TO PUT THE LID ON.

NEVER MIND CHOCOLATE HEAVEN... THIS IS TURNING INTO CHOCOLATE HELL!
????!!!!
YEEAAARGH! EEEEEEEEEEEEK!
OVER THERE!
IT'S A MOUSE!
WHAT'S THE MATTER?!
AW, SO IT IS. HE'S CUTE! LOOK AT HIS LITTLE EYES...

JUST GET IT OUT!
NOT FOR ME, SILLY! MICE LOVE CHOCOLATE, TOO. I CAN GET HIM INTO MY HAND WITH IT AND CATCH HIM.

GIVE ME A PIECE OF CHOCOLATE THEN.
THIS IS NO TIME TO BE SNACKING!

C'MON, MISTER. HAVE A LITTLE NIBBLE...

ANIMAL-LOVING EMMA SOON HAS THE MOUSE EATING OUT OF HER HAND...!
YEEEEEEEK! STOP IT!
HERE HE IS. DO YOU WANT TO HAVE A HOLD?
DAD CALLING
IN THE CHAOS, SINDY DOESN'T HEAR HER MOBILE PHONE...
THANKS, EMMA. NOW...WHAT WAS I DOING?
WHAT ARE THOSE GIRLS LIKE? I'LL JUST GO AND PUT THIS LITTLE FELLA OUTSIDE, THEN I'LL DO SOME POPCORN.
SINDY COMES BACK TO CLEAN UP THE LIVING ROOM, BUT...
HIP HOP!
SALSA!
HIP HOP!
SALSA!

COME ON, YOU GUYS. LET'S NOT ARGUE ABOUT WHAT MUSIC TO PUT ON. WE CAN LISTEN TO BOTH.
SALSA FIRST THEN!
HIP HOP FIRST!

BUT YOU SAID YOUR MUM AND DAD WOULDN'T BE BACK FOR AGES!
ANYWAY, ROSA, I THOUGHT YOU WERE MEANT TO BE CLEARING UP THE KITCHEN. IT'S A COMPLETE TIP!

WELL, I DID... I MEAN THEY WON'T, BUT...
BACK IN THE KITCHEN.......
HOW MUCH DID YOU PUT IN?
IS THE MICROWAVEABLE POPCORN SUPPOSED TO DO THAT?
SINDY! COME, QUICK!

JUST THE ONE...
BOX!
TOO RIGHT. WHAT'S THAT SMELL?
YOU MEAN SIX BAGS... OH, LOOK AT THE STATE OF THIS PLACE! WE'RE GOING TO HAVE TO START TIDYING UP.

BUT.......
OH, NO! ROSA'S COOKIES!
I'D BETTER GET THEM OUT QUICK. YOW!
CRASH

HELLO-O-O! IS EVERYTHING ALL RIGHT?.........
ULP! MUM'S BACK!
MUM! DAD! YOU'RE BACK EARLY!
LOOK AT THE MESS IN HERE! PLEASE TELL ME THAT'S NOT NAIL VARNISH...
WELL, THE NEIGHBOURS CALLED TO SAY THEY HEARD SCREAMING AND WE COULDN'T GET AN ANSWER ON YOUR MOBILE. ARE YOU ALL OKAY?
MUM, I'M SO SORRY. THE KITCHEN'S A TIP AS WELL. I DON'T KNOW HOW IT ALL HAPPENED...
DO YOU KNOW HOW TO GET NAIL POLISH OUT, BY ANY CHANCE?
WE'RE SORRY, TOO, MRS BAXTER. PLEASE DON'T BE CROSS...
WE'LL CLEAR EVERYTHING UP RIGHT AWAY!!
SINDY AND ROSA SET TO WORK IN THE KITCHEN..........

...WHILE MYA, EMMA AND LILLI SORT OUT THE LIVING ROOM........
I THINK THAT'S DONE IT.

FINISHED AT LAST......
WELL, AS I'M GLAD YOU'RE ALL SAFE AND YOU'VE DONE A GOOD JOB OF CLEANING UP, YOU CAN HAVE THE TREAT I BROUGHT BACK FROM THE RESTAURANT...

CHOCOLATE MICE! FOR YOUR CHOCOLATE NIGHT!

CHOCOLATE...? MICE...? NO THANKS!!

Pillow Fight

A sleepover isn't a sleepover if the girls don't have a pillow fight! Look carefully at these pictures of Sindy and her sleepover friends to see if you can spot the five differences in the second picture. The answers are at the bottom of the page.

Answers: 1. There is a feather missing. 2. A cup of hot chocolate has appeared. 3. PomPom the penguin has moved. 4. An eye mask has appeared. 5. Pickles the teddy is missing.

Potty About Popcorn

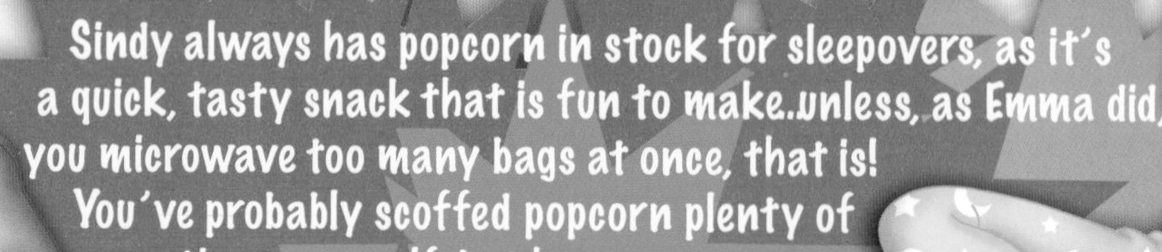

Sindy always has popcorn in stock for sleepovers, as it's a quick, tasty snack that is fun to make..unless, as Emma did, you microwave too many bags at once, that is! You've probably scoffed popcorn plenty of times yourself, but have you ever wondered what makes it pop? Read on to find out and you'll also discover some other interesting nuggets - or kernels - of popcorn info!

Magic Moisture

As popcorn needs the drop of water inside it to pop, it should be stored carefully so it doesn't dry out. Never keep your popping corn in the fridge! The best way to store it is in a plastic or glass container with a lid, kept in a cupboard.

How Does It Do That?

The secret of popcorn popping is a tiny drop of water in the middle of it. This is inside a shell of soft starch, which in turn sits inside the hard kernel. As it heats up, the water drop gets bigger and turns into steam. The pressure from the steam makes the soft starch burst through the hard kernel so that the steam can escape. So, what you have in your bowl or box is a whole heap of inside-out kernels of corn!

Lonely Kern

Ever noticed those of corn that don't po These are known a old maids or spinsters, which are old-fashioned words for women that have not married. That's charming, that is!

Popcorn Culture

People in the United States of America eat more popcorn than anyone else in the world.
That may be because most of the world's popping corn is grown there!

That's The Spirit!

Native American Indians used to say that there was a spirit living in each kernel that jumped out angrily when its house was heated!
Oo-er

Popcorn Of Old

The oldest popping corn ever discovered was in a cave in New Mexico in 1950. It was found to be about 4,000 years old. Just a bit stale, then!

Sweet Or Sandy?

Popcorn has been around for thousands of years. In the days before cookers, one way to pop corn was to heat sand in a fire and stir the popping corn in when the sand was really hot. Tasty!

Pretty Popcorn

As well as using popcorn for food, Aztec Indians used it to make decorative headdresses and necklaces. Next time you have some popcorn, take a close look at it. Kinda pretty, isn't it? You could try making it into funky things yourself!

Pillow Hopping

Sindy's fluffy pillows are good for a fight, but they're great for this pillow-hopping game, too! Grab a dice and counters and you can join in with a friend.

Put a counter for each player on Emma's Flopsey bunny and take turns to throw the dice ONCE each turn. To bunny hop to the first pillow, you must wait until you throw a one on the dice. To hop to pillow number 2, you must throw a two on the dice, and so on. Carry on until you reach the last pillow, throwing a six to land on it.The player to reach the last pillow first is the lucky winner of some yummy chocs! Happy hopping!

Cuddly Cookie

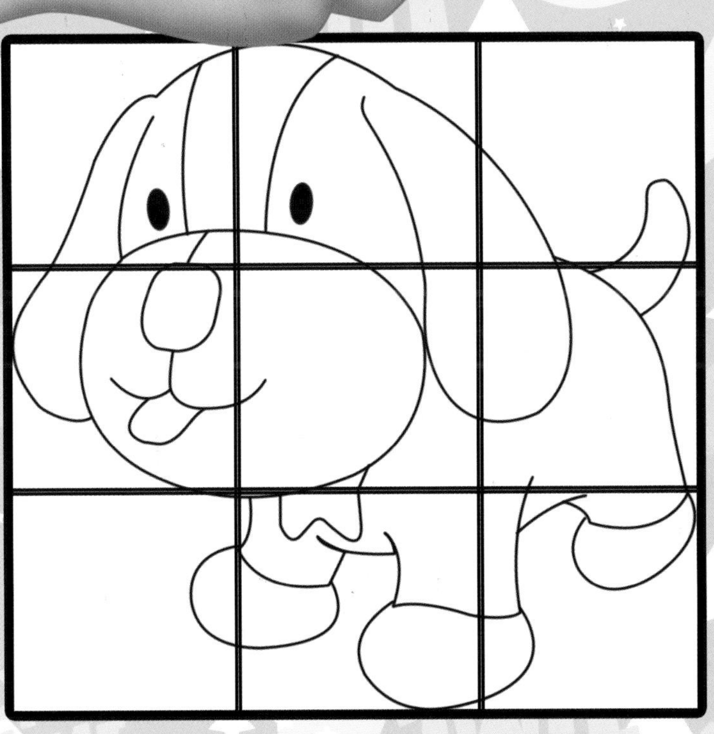

The girls just can't get to sleep without their cuddlies! Mya's favourite is Cookie the dog. Use a pencil to draw him into the second grid by copying the first grid, square by square. We've started Cookie off to help you! When you've drawn him, use your pens or pencils to colour him in. Isn't he cute?

Why don't you try this drawing trick with your cuddlies?

Take a picture of your favourite teddy and divide it into squares.
Then copy the same amount of squares onto some plain paper.
Fill in the squares you have just created by copying from the squares on your photograph.
By changing the size of the squares, you can make your copy as big as you want!

Sindy's Dream Wedding

Mya, Emma, Rosa and Lilli were on their way over to Sindy's house.
"What do you think Sindy's so excited about?" Emma wondered.
"I don't know," said Lilli. "She said she had something to show us."
"Maybe she's got one of those cool new phones we were talking about at school," suggested Emma. They rang Sindy's doorbell and waited.
"Ta-daaaa!" exclaimed Sindy as she opened the door and spread out her arms. The girls all gasped: she was wearing the most beautiful bridesmaid's dress they had ever seen.
"Sindy, that's gorgeous!" shrieked Lilli, hurrying inside and walking all the way round her friend to see the dress from every angle. "Is it for your cousin's wedding tomorrow?"
"Well, I wasn't thinking of coming to school in it," teased Sindy.

The girls went into the living room and huddled around Sindy, feeling the silky dress and adjusting her lacy headpiece.
"Does anyone want to try it on?" she asked.
"Me!" four voices cried in unison.
"Be careful with it, though," Sindy added. "I only got it back today after it was altered. If I spoil it I'll be in big trouble!"
Sindy let Lilli try on the gown first, then each of the others took a turn. They all agreed that the outfit looked fabulous on everyone.
"Okay, I'd better hang it up again," said Sindy. "I don't want anything happening to it before the morning."
Sindy hung the dress up on her wardrobe door and stared at it that night before she drifted off to sleep...

"Sindy! Sindy, wake up! You'll be late for the wedding!"
Sindy sat up in bed, puzzled. She felt like she hadn't been asleep long. Smiling at her was Rosa, dressed in a bridesmaid's dress.
"Why are you dressed like that?" Sindy asked. "I'm the bridesmaid, not you."
"Have you forgotten already?" chuckled Rosa. "Your cousin said we could all be bridesmaids, remember? She came round with these lovely dresses for us."
Sindy rubbed her eyes as Mya, Emma and Lilli trotted into her room in their silky gowns and danced around her bed.
"You look lovely," she told them. "What time is it?"

"It's Lilli time!" cackled Lilli, jumping on the covers. Sindy slid out of bed and wondered why her friend was acting so strangely.

Once Sindy had got her dress on, she went downstairs to see where the others were. She found them in the kitchen, using the blender.
"Here you go, Sindy," said Emma. "You've just got time for a nice smoothie."
Sindy thanked her friend and took a sip of the drink.
"This tastes of onion!" she spluttered.
"I had to use onions because you didn't have any strawberries," Rosa explained. "Then I had to use tomato sauce to make it red."
Sindy looked in disbelief at Rosa, then gasped as Emma dropped her smoothie on Mya's dress.
"My dress!" shrieked Mya. "It's ruined!"
"Why are we having these after we've got our dresses on, anyway?" Sindy asked, exasperated.

Emma rubbed a cloth on the dress and the red splodge magically disappeared.
"There, nothing to make a fuss about," she grinned. "Now, come on. Time to go!"
The girls rushed out of Sindy's house. Emma was the last to leave and slammed the door on to her dress without realising. She dashed away and there was a loud R-R-R-I-I-P! Sindy heard it and gasped.
"Oh, Emma!" she exclaimed, hurrying over and opening the door to get the dress out.
"That's torn it!" giggled Emma.
"But look at the state of your dress," said Sindy. "Aren't you bothered?"
"It's all right," Emma insisted cheerfully. She tied the loose bits in a big knot. "There, that looks fine now. Let's go!"

As they were leaving, a pair of decorators arrived.
"You must be Sindy," smiled one of them. "We've come to paint the outside of your house. Your dad said lime green with pink stars, is that right?"
Sindy looked blankly at him and wondered where her dad was.
"I don't think so...I mean, I don't know. I haven't got time for this, I'm trying to get to a wedding!"
"Sindy! Watch out!" shouted Mya. Sindy spun round to be greeted by the neighbour's dog. It was covered in mud and was jumping up at her, trying to lick her face. Its wet, dirty paws skidded all over her dress.
"Get down!" she shrieked. "Get off me!"
The two decorators grabbed the dog and held its collar.

"What am I going to do?" wailed Sindy. "I can't go to a wedding like this!"
"Don't worry about it," said one of the decorators, opening a can of paint. "We can just paint over the mucky bits." Before Sindy could argue, he knelt at her feet and began to paint over the paw marks.
"That...that's pink paint!" gasped Sindy. "My dress is white!"
"Pink and white go together nicely, don't they, girls?"
"Ooh, yes," nodded Sindy's friends. Sindy looked at them open-mouthed, wondering if they were going mad...or maybe she was.
"There, all done," said the man, standing up. "Not bad, even if I do say so myself."
Sindy looked down in horror at the pink paint splodges on her dress.

“Aw, she likes it so much she can’t speak,” giggled Mya.
“We’re late, we’re late, for a very important date!” sang Lilli. “Hurry, hurry, hurry!”
Sindy’s friends trotted off down the street, holding up their dresses.
“I thought we were going by car!” Sindy called after them. “It’s miles to the wedding!”
“No, we’re walking,” Rosa called back. “Well, running.”
Sindy caught up with her friends, just as the tune of Nelly The Elephant blasted in her ear.
“It’s the ice cream man!” shrieked Emma. “Stop, everyone. I need a 99!”
Emma and the others huddled round the ice cream van, wondering what to have.
“Aren’t we supposed be rushing to the wedding?” Sindy asked, trying not to shout impatiently.

“Chill out, Sindy,” smiled Rosa. “What do you want, ice cream or lolly?”
“I don’t want anything,” Sindy snapped. “Please hurry up!”
She watched in amazement as her friends sauntered over to a bench with their ice creams and sat down to eat them.
“You do realise you’re making us even later,” she told them.
“Later for what?” asked Mya.
“THE WEDDING!” replied Sindy.
“All right, no need to get grumpy,” said Emma. “Come on, girls, down in one.”
Emma, Mya, Rosa and Lilli put their ice creams in their mouths and swallowed them whole in one gulp.
“H-h-how did you do that?” spluttered Sindy.
“Do what?” smiled Lilli, jumping up and taking Sindy’s hand. “Come on!”

The girls carried on running down the street.
"Let's go this way," Rosa called out, "it's quicker."
Rosa led the others down a tree-lined path. The further they went down it, the more trees there were. Ferns began to appear at the girls' feet.
"The path's disappearing," complained Sindy, slowing down and fighting her way through what was now a jungle. "Are you sure this is the right way?"
She screamed as a snake slithered past her feet and disappeared in the undergrowth.
"It's a short cut! It's a short cut!" squawked a red and blue parrot, swooping down low over her head.
"Where ARE we?" Sindy cried.
"Not far to go now," replied Rosa, breaking up a huge cobweb that blocked the path.

At last they came out of the trees, on to the most beautiful beach Sindy had ever seen.
"Oh, I think we took a wrong turning," said Rosa. "Is there something on my back?"
"Keep still," said Emma, scooping up a tarantula while Sindy watched nervously through her fingers. Keeping her hands cupped around the huge spider, Emma took it back to the trees and put it gently on the ground.
"That's it, back into the jungle you go," she cooed.
Mya and Lilli began to paddle in the sea, letting the hems of their dresses get wet.
"It's really warm," Lilli called to the others. "Come and try it!"
"But what about the wedding?" Sindy called to them.
"WHAT ABOUT THE WEDDING?"

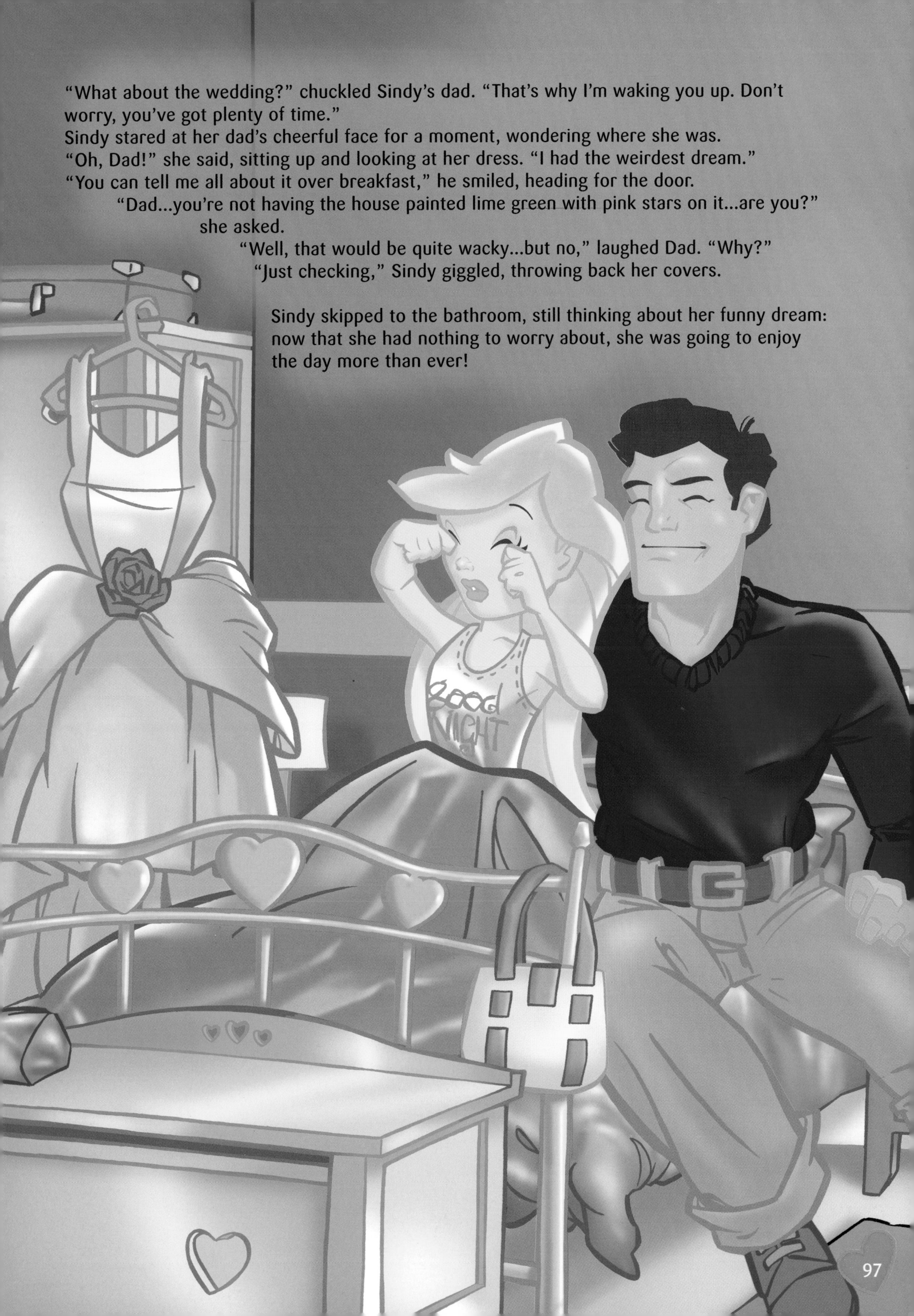

"What about the wedding?" chuckled Sindy's dad. "That's why I'm waking you up. Don't worry, you've got plenty of time."
Sindy stared at her dad's cheerful face for a moment, wondering where she was.
"Oh, Dad!" she said, sitting up and looking at her dress. "I had the weirdest dream."
"You can tell me all about it over breakfast," he smiled, heading for the door.
"Dad...you're not having the house painted lime green with pink stars on it...are you?" she asked.
"Well, that would be quite wacky...but no," laughed Dad. "Why?"
"Just checking," Sindy giggled, throwing back her covers.

Sindy skipped to the bathroom, still thinking about her funny dream: now that she had nothing to worry about, she was going to enjoy the day more than ever!

Naturally Nice Nails

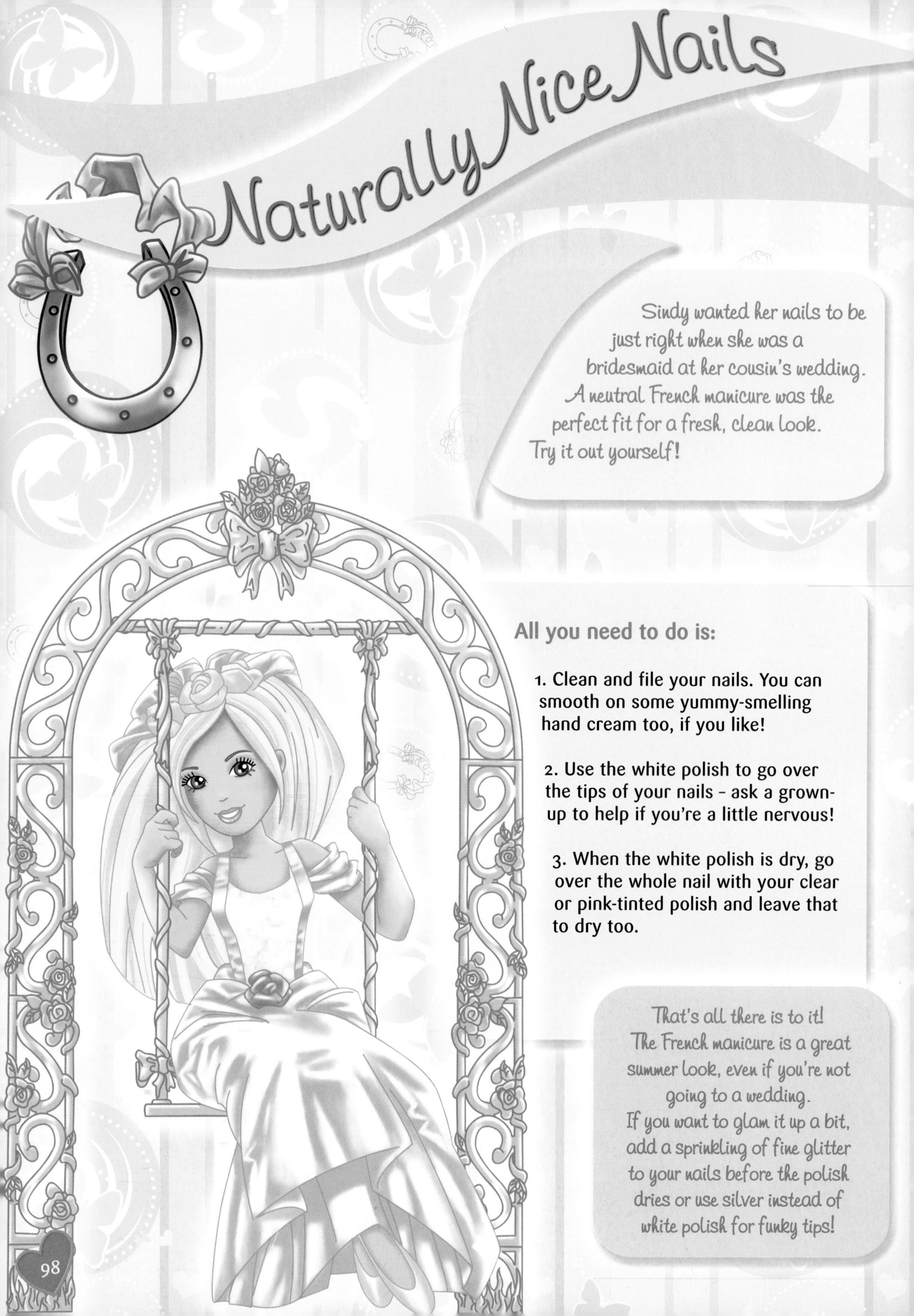

Sindy wanted her nails to be just right when she was a bridesmaid at her cousin's wedding. A neutral French manicure was the perfect fit for a fresh, clean look. Try it out yourself!

All you need to do is:

1. Clean and file your nails. You can smooth on some yummy-smelling hand cream too, if you like!
2. Use the white polish to go over the tips of your nails - ask a grown-up to help if you're a little nervous!
3. When the white polish is dry, go over the whole nail with your clear or pink-tinted polish and leave that to dry too.

That's all there is to it!
The French manicure is a great summer look, even if you're not going to a wedding.
If you want to glam it up a bit, add a sprinkling of fine glitter to your nails before the polish dries or use silver instead of white polish for funky tips!

How Many Horseshoes?

Sindy and her friends have been given the chance to be bridesmaids, this time for real! How many lucky horseshoes can you find in the picture? The answer is at the bottom of the page.

Answer: There are eight lucky horseshoes.

Lucky Emma

Join the dots to see what bridesmaid Emma is trying to catch for good luck! Then use your crayons or pencils to colour the picture.

Wedding Lines

Sindy and her friends are just loving their day as bridesmaids! Look carefully at these things from the wedding reception and draw a circle round the odd one out in each row.

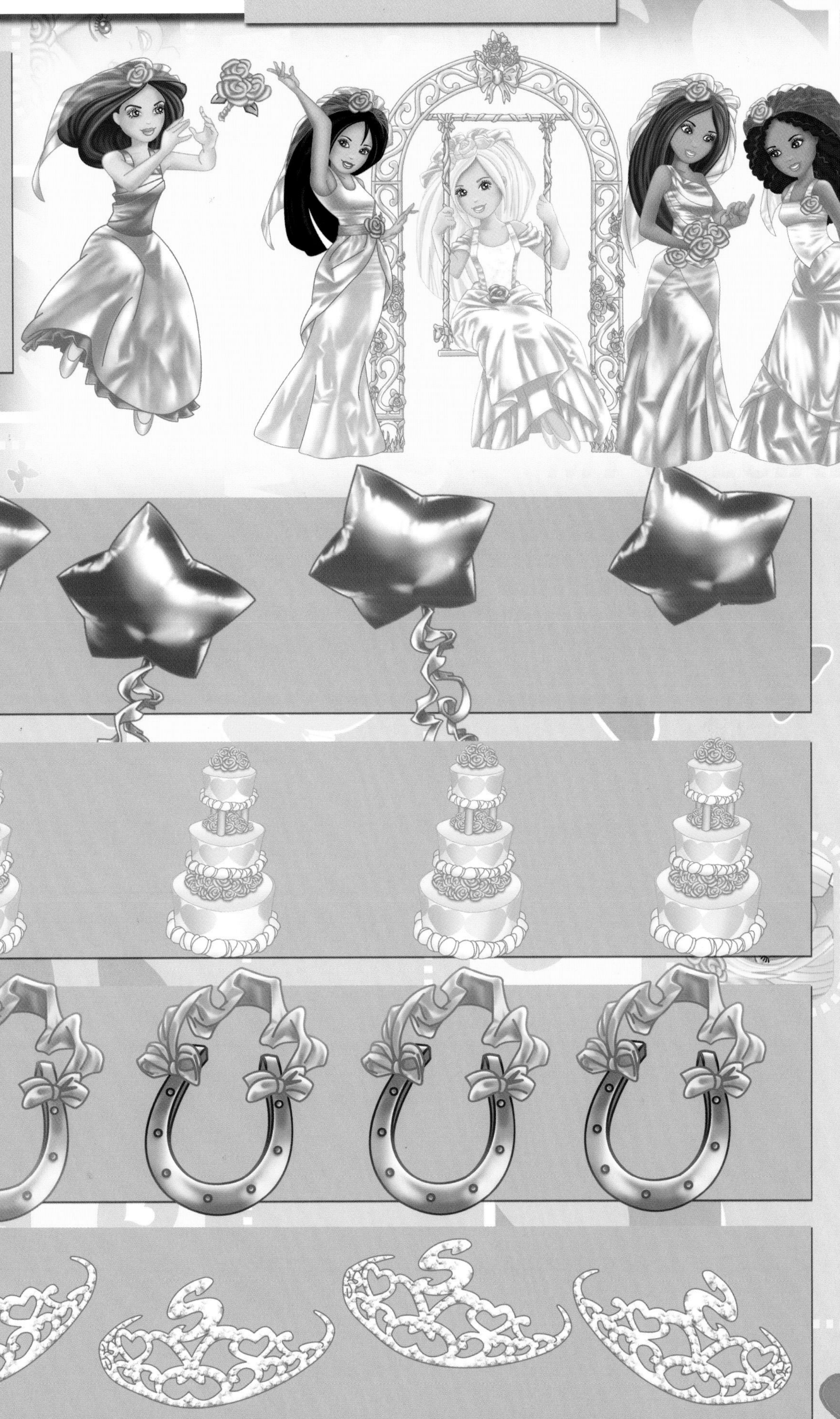

This Way Wedding

The wedding photos are almost over and now it's time for some wedding cake. Join Sindy and her friends in their race to get the first piece!

Each player chooses a counter and places it on the start. Take turns to throw the dice and work your way round the spaces, making sure you throw a six to start.

The first player to reach the wedding cake to grab the first slice is the winner!

For Cake
6
7
8
9
10 Balloons block your way! Miss a turn.
11
12
13
14
15
16
17
18
19
20 A lucky horseshoe! Go on two spaces.
35
36 You stop to catch the bouquet! Miss a turn!
37
38
39
40 Finish!

Colouring Competition

Hi, look at this gorgeus picture of me dressed as a beautiful bride!
Why don't you make me look even more special by colouring in my dress with some pretty colours, patterns, and dont forget my swing!
Why don't you stick little paper roses on it for a cool 3D effect?!

When you have finished, complete yout details on the back of the page and send it to me at the address shown!
I will then choose my favourite.
Good luck, and see what you could win!

The 10 best entries will receive a Sindy's Busy Breakfast Bar Playset!

Sindy loves to make yummy treats for her friends when they come to visit in her very own Busy Breakfast Bar!

This kitchen is fully of funky gadgets for Sindy to create delicious smoothies and tasty treats, while Sindy's friends can sit at the breakfast bar enjoying t hem!

The 30 runners up will each receive a Hair Extensions Sindy.

Sindy loves to keep up with the latest fashion trends and sometimes even Sindy wants to change her hair style!

With the special hair extensions Sindy's hair can change from short to long. There are even funky coloured hair pieces for Sindy to wear when she is going to a party!

COLOUR AND CONTENT MAY VARY.

Colour me in!

Colouring Competition

When you have finished making me beautiful for my special day, please carefuly cut out this page, put it in a large envelope. and then send it to me at the address below.

Sindy Annual 2007 Competition
Pedigree Books
Beech Hill House
Walnut Gardens
Exeter
Devon
EX4 4DH

Don't forget to put a stamp on your envelope!
The Post Office will not deliver unstamped entries

Now ask a grown-up to help you out with this section

Name...

Age...

Address...

....

Telephone Number...................................

The closing date for entries is the end of Febuary 2007

The 40 winning entries will be selected by our editorial staff. Each winner will be notified by post and sent their prize. The winning pictures will appear in next year's Sindy Annual. Rules of entry: Entries are limited to one per person. You do not need to have purchased the annual to enter. Entries cannot be returned. The organiser's decision is final and no correspondence shall be entered into. Employees of Pedigree or any one connected with the production of this annual cannot enter.

Sindy loves...

I love doing cool and interesting things, and I have a very active imagination so I can sometimes daydream myself into some crazy situations! A you are my friend, I thought I would share these with you!!

I love dancing, it is definitely my favourite hobby and sport as it keeps me so fit! This is me in my dance clothes warming up for a tough class ahead, Miss Ghost is my dance teacher and she can be really tough!!

This is me ready for bed wearing my fave PJ's. I am chatting to one of the girls on my mobile phone before going to sleep - we are probably checking our homework! I love my bed, it is soooo comfy and there is just enough room for me to share it with Pickles my favourite teddy bear.

This is my favourite car in the whole wide world - it is a hot pink Mini-car and I love it soooo much! Actually I love all things that are pink, as you can see my mobile phone MP3 player are pink too!

This is how I imagination myself in my favourite daydream - I am Sindy the Fairy Princess and live in a magical world filled with unicorns and rainbows!! I love the floaty dress I am wearing - it is truly magical!

All these products can be bought at Woolworths.......

Sindy.com

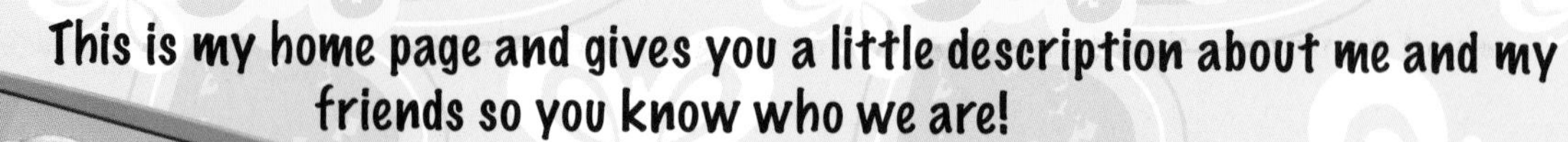

This is my home page and gives you a little description about me and my friends so you know who we are!
I haven't added Rosa yet as she is still deciding what picture she wants included!

Hi! I'm Sindy and I love shopping, fashion, music and hanging out with my friends. I like anything pink and enjoy singing and dancing. I love being on stage!

home photos fun news diary join in art win

This is my diary page, where I write about all the fun things I've been doing and where I share all my secrets! The page you can see in the picture was when I wrote about my mum's birthday. I update it often so if you want to know what I'm doing then this is the place to be!

This is the page where you can enter your details and become part of the Sindy club for free!

Hi there! Just like my friends, I enjoy going on to the internet looking for interesting websites and keeping in touch with friends via email. To make sure everyone knew was I was doing I created my own website - why don't you have a look?

This is the fun section, where there are games to play, cards to send to your friends and screensavers to download for your own computer! These games are my favourites ever - I especially like the makeover game where I can try lots of different looks and styles!

My news page is a lot of fun as I have asked Lilli and Mya to help with this! Each month I suggest something you 'must do', Lilli suggests a 'must-have', and Mya tells you something you 'must know' which is usually a crazy fact!

By joining you get a birthday card and a newsletter each month which has its own competitions to win super cool Sindy prizes!

Hi, Look at this fab picture of me singing at my favourite place - the Karaoke Café! Why don't you make me look like a pop star by colouring in my clothes with some really funky styles and patterns.....and don't forget the glitter to make me really sparkle!!
When you have finished, don't forget to complete your details on the back of this page and send it to me at the address shown! Good luck,
Sindy x
STAR
COOL BABE
FUNKY